Horrid Henry
Annual 2019

Horrid Henry
Annual 2019

Francesca Simon

Illustrated by Tony Ross

Orion
Children's Books

ORION CHILDREN'S BOOKS

First published in Great Britain in 2018
by Hodder and Stoughton

1 3 5 7 9 10 8 6 4 2

This compilation, Horrid Henry's Annual 2019 © Orion Children's Books 2018
Text © Francesca Simon 2018
Illustrations © Tony Ross 2018

Compiled by Sally Byford from the Horrid Henry books
by Francesca Simon and illustrated by Tony Ross

The moral rights of the author and illustrator have been asserted.

A CIP catalogue record for this book
is available from the British Library.

ISBN 978 1 5101 0519 5

Printed and bound in China

The paper and board used in this book
are from well-managed forests and other responsible sources.

MIX
Paper from
responsible sources
FSC® C104740
FSC
www.fsc.org

Orion Children's Books
An imprint of
Hachette Children's Group
Part of Hodder and Stoughton
Carmelite House
50 Victoria Embankment
London EC4Y 0DZ

An Hachette UK Company
www.hachette.co.uk
www.hachettechildrens.co.uk
www.horridhenry.co.uk

Contents

Hello Henry Fans and Purple Hand Gang Members!

A new Horrid Henry annual – what a happy day! Well, it would be if my real parents, the King and Queen, would stop trying on their crowns and admiring their jewels and come and RESCUE ME. Yes, rescue me from the imposters who pretend to be related to me.

Think *your* family is horrid? That your brothers and sisters are the wormiest worms on the planet? That your mum is the strictest and your dad is the meanest? Think again! No one has a meaner, more horrible family than me. No one. No one has a cousin more stuck-up than Steve, or a toady tell-tale brother toadier than Peter. And don't get me started on frog-face Margaret and Sour Puss Susan. Ughhhhh.

But all is not lost. You need help from a master of parent taming and brother squashing and friend wrangling. This annual contains some of my greatest ever tricks to show my family and friends who is boss.
ME, of course.

You'll discover handy tips for ensuring any shopping or car trip is a disaster, and how to make extra sure you are never dragged out for a walk in the (blecccchhhh) countryside again. Get out of chores! Be crowned Ruler of the World! Be left in peace to lie on the sofa, eat crisps and watch telly. Until the happy day when the Queen's carriage pulls up, at least you won't have to empty the bins or lose control of the TV remote.

Henry

Spot the Baa Baa Sheepies

CLUE:
Fluff Puff has a pink and yellow nose.

Horrid Henry has pinched Perfect Peter's little sheepies. They are hidden around the annual – how many can you find?
One of the sheepies is Fluff Puff, Peter's favourite.
Which page is Fluff Puff on?
The answers are on page 58.

My Family: Who's Who

ME!
Lord High Excellent Majesty of the Family of Horrid Henry. Leader of the Purple Hand Gang. Undiscovered genius.

MUM AND DAD
The most mean and miserable parents in the whole world. They like camping, hiking, vegetables and tiny TVs.

FANG
My pet hamster. He's a lot less boring than the rest of my family.

PERFECT PETER
My little brother. He likes TV programmes for babies, helping Mum and Dad with chores and doing his homework. Yeuch! What a slimy worm and a wibble pants.

FLUFFY
Fat old Fluffy is allowed to do nothing all the time. It's not fair!

GRANDMA
Grandma is Mum's mum. She eats lots of chocolate and brings me fantastic presents that Mum and Dad don't let me have, like Tyrannosaur Dinosaur Roars.

RICH AUNT RUBY and STUCK-UP STEVE

Rich Aunt Ruby is Mum's posh sister who lives in a big, old house. Stuck-up Steve is my slimy cousin – the yuckiest boy that ever slithered around on this earth.

SOME OTHER OLD PEOPLE

GREAT-AUNT GRETA

She thinks I'm a girl and sends me the worst presents in the world, like the Walkie-Talkie-Burpy-Slurpy-Teasy-Weasy Doll – which was even worse than the lime-green cardigan from Rich Aunt Ruby.

GRANNY and GRANDPA

Dad's mum is old and bossy, and Dad's dad is old and sleepy.

PRISSY POLLY, PIMPLY PAUL and VOMITING VERA

Prissy Polly is my cousin too. Isn't one enough? Polly is always squeaking, and she's married to Pimply Paul who has huge spots all over his ugly face. They have a stinky, wailing baby called Vomiting Vera.

One day my real parents, the King and Queen, will take me home to the palace, where no one ever says, "Don't be horrid, Henry!"

HORRiD HENRY'S Whodunnit Quiz

Each of the family members below has committed a horrible crime. Do you know WHO did WHAT?

DAD	MUM	PETER	RICH AUNT RUBY	GREAT-AUNT GRETA	STUCK-UP STEVE	PRISSY POLLY	PIMPLY PAUL

1. WHO made me eat at Restaurant Le Posh?

2. WHO tried to scare me at night?

3. WHO made me go shopping and forced me to try on girls' trousers?

4. WHO sent me these frilly pink lacy knickers?

5. WHO made me be a pageboy at her wedding and forced me to wear the silliest clothes ever?

_____

6. WHO dared to call me a little brat?

_____

7. WHO is always telling me to turn down my boom-box?

_____

8. WHO wrote a love letter to Moody Margaret and pretended it was from me?

_____

Check the answers on page 58 to find your score.

How did you do?

6-8: A fantastic score! Well done at working out which of my mean and miserable family have committed these hideous crimes!

3-5: A medium mark – did you get in a muddle with who'd done what?!

0-2: Mega-congratulations must go to you! You know nothing about my family – lucky you!!

HORRID HENRY'S Invasion

Peter had run blabbing to Mum that Henry had watched *Mutant Max* and *Knight Fight* when Mum had said he could only watch one or the other. Henry had been banned from watching TV all day. Peter was such a telltale frogface ninnyhammer toady poo bag, thought Horrid Henry grimly. Well, just wait till Peter tried to colour in his new picture, he'd—

"MUM!" screamed Peter. "Henry switched the caps on my coloured pens. I just put pink in the sky."

"Didn't!" yelled Henry.

"Did!" wailed Peter.

"Prove it," said Horrid Henry, smirking.

Mum came upstairs. Quickly Henry leapt over the mess covering the floor of his room, flopped on the bed and grabbed a *Screamin' Demon* comic. Peter came and stood in the doorway.

"Henry's being horrid," snivelled Peter.

"Henry, have you been in Peter's room?" said Mum.

Henry sighed loudly. "Of course I've been in his smelly room. I live here, don't I?"

"I mean when he wasn't here," said Mum.

"No," said Horrid Henry. This wasn't a lie, because even if Peter *wasn't* there his horrible stinky smell was.

"He has too," said Peter. "Fluff Puff was turned the wrong way round."

"Maybe he was just trying to escape from your pongy pants," said Henry. "*I* would."

"Mum!" said Peter.

"Henry! Don't be horrid. Leave your brother alone."

"I *am* leaving him alone," said Horrid Henry.

"Why can't he leave *me* alone? And get out of *my* room, Peter!" he shrieked, as Peter put his foot just inside Henry's door.

Peter quickly withdrew his foot.

Henry glared at Peter.

Peter glared at Henry.

Mum sighed. "The next one who goes into the other's room without permission will be banned from the computer for a week. And no pocket money either."

She turned to go.

Henry stuck out his tongue at Peter.

"Tell-tale," he mouthed.

"Mum!" screamed Peter.

Does Henry sneak into Peter's room – or does Peter creep into Henry's room? Find out in 'Horrid Henry's Invasion' from *Horrid Henry Rocks*.

HORRiD HENRY'S Guide to Catching a Sneaky Peeker

Here are my top tips and traps to trick Peter if he dares to sneak into my room.

1. Leave the bedroom door slightly open, and balance a bucket or bowl of water on top. When Peter pushes the door open – **WHOOSH!** – he'll be soaked! Serve him right!

2. Tie a web of string criss-crossing from the bedpost to the door to ensnare this unwelcome worm.

3. Scatter some whoopee cushions strategically on the floor. That will stop Peter creeping about quietly! **POOP! POOP!**

4. Rub shoe polish on the drawer and cupboard handles. Peter will be so busy sneaking and peeking, he won't spot it – until it's all over his hands, **HA HA!**

5. Use sticky tape to tape up drawers. If the tape gets moved or snapped, it's perfect proof that sneaky peeker Peter has been poking into them.

6. Place a tempting-looking diary so it peeps out from under the bed. Write 'DIARY –TOP SECRET– KEEP OUT!' on the cover. Peter won't be able to resist it. On the front page, leave him a message: GOTCHA! YOU'RE A WIBBLE BIBBLE WORM!

WARNING! Don't forget you've laid the traps!

17

Can you match the jigsaw pieces below to the spaces
in the picture of Horrid Henry's bedroom?

1. = 4 ___

2. = ___

3. = ___

4. = ___

5. = ___

6. = ___

7. = ___

The answers are on page 58.

How To Control Your Parents

Taming your parents is a breeze. Just remember who is in charge . . . you! If your family dog can rule the house with a few strategic barks and whimpers, think what YOU can do, once you remember a few handy rules.

1. **Don't let your parents know you're the boss.** I can promise you, they won't like it. The secret is to get your OWN way, without letting them in on the top secret that they are pawns in your hands. BWWAAAAAHAHAHAHA!

2. **Shame and Tame.** You'll be shocked to know that all parents think they're perfect. So anyone who questions their perfection immediately has the upper hand. Just make sure you talk about how BRILLIANT and WONDERFUL your friends' parents are. How they let their kids stay up late. Give tons of pocket money. Hand them sweets night and day and let them have chocolate fudge sauce and whipped cream on ice cream every night. Your parents won't want anyone to think they are losers in the perfect parents competition. They'll be eager to behave better. Just watch.

3. **Praise good behaviour.** If you want to keep your parents on the right path, you need to thank and praise them. This is very important. Even horrible, mean parents like mine OCCASIONALLY do the right thing. Everyone, even old battle-axes, like a bit of praise. So don't hold back. Soon, your piggy bank will explode with all the extra pocket money you'll be getting.

4. **Bore and nag them to death.** Go on and on and on and on and on and on and on until your parents will give you anything just for a bit of peace. So whine away like your life depends on it. Tantrums can also help, especially in public.

5. **Imagine your parents are toddlers.** Annoying, bossy toddlers. You already know how to tame irritating younger brothers and sisters. (And if YOU are the younger one, you can still try some of my tricks on that mean big brother and sister. Just 'cause they're bigger doesn't ALWAYS mean they are smarter.)

How Tame Are Your Parents?

Follow the flowchart and find out!

Pocket Money Puzzles

Horrid Henry thinks he deserves loads more pocket money.
But does he get any less than his arch enemy,
Moody Margaret, or his slimy cousin, Stuck-up Steve?
Use the clues to find out – and to discover which toy
they most want to spend their money on.

POCKET MONEY: 50p, £5.00, £10.00
TOYS: Demon Dagger Sabre, Super-Blooper Blaster,
Hip-Hop Robot Dog

	HOW MUCH POCKET MONEY?	DREAM TOY
HORRID HENRY		
MOODY MARGARET		
STUCK-UP STEVE		

For Sale
£5.00

CLUES

1. Horrid Henry gets the smallest amount of pocket money. It's not fair!

2. The one who gets the most pocket money wants to buy the Super-Blooper Blaster.

3. Moody Margaret wants to buy the Demon Dagger Sabre.

Henry's top-secret plans to make some cold, hard cash

Sell Peter = **50p**

Raid Peter's piggy bank = **£1.50**

Collect for my favourite charity, Child in Need = **90p**

Hold Peter's Bunnykins for ransom = **£2.10**

GRAND TOTAL = £5.00 !! YES!!!

Check out the answers on page 58.

How Horrid Henry Fools His Family

TECHNO TAKEOVER

I'm such a whizz with technology, it's easy-peasy to trick my parents. They are so old and doddery, they are completely clueless about computers. All I had to do was pop a secret password in the computer – and I was the only one who could use it! When they needed to catch up with their work, I offered to save the day and get it working again, and they promised to give me anything I asked for. Result!

It's important to have complete control of the TV remote too. Our household rule is the first person in the Comfy Black Chair controls the TV remote. So it's simple – all I have to do is make sure I'm first in the chair by getting up extra early. If this tactic fails, and that toad Perfect Peter starts getting up even earlier than me, I have another top tactic – putting my favourite channel on, and hiding the remote, ha ha!

AVOIDING CHORES

Do your parents make you do boring chores at the weekend, like mine do? It's not fair – that's what they are there for! One of my most amazing tricks is to leave the hoover roaring away – then sneak off to watch TV in secret, tee hee! Once, I put a red sweatshirt into the white wash by accident – and when Dad discovered that all his underpants, shirts and vests were pink, I was never asked to do the washing again. Sorted!

SICK DAYS

If Perfect Peter is coughing and spluttering and pretending to be poorly, he gets a day off school. Well, I want a day off too. Coughing loudly a lot gets my parents' attention. Clutching at my poor sore throat, complaining that everything aches, and wailing that I'm going to be sick might do the trick. If not, then I have to do loads of moaning and groaning until they finally give in and say the magic words: "All right, you can stay at home." Hooray! *Mutant Max* and *Robot Rebels* here I come!

GETTING RID OF UNWANTED GUESTS

Sometimes something so horrible happens that it takes a genius mind like mine to sort it out. Like that time that Moody Margaret came to stay – for TWO whole weeks, while her parents went on holiday. Moody Margaret moaned that our house wasn't very clean, she screamed when supper wasn't ready at six o'clock, she spat out her food because Dad put salt on it, and she played her trumpet at six o'clock in the morning.

It was time for action! I crept to the phone one night and secretly left a message. The next day, Margaret's mum and dad rushed back from their holiday because they'd had a message about an emergency, and they took Margaret home. Hooray! So I fooled both my family and Moody Margaret's family! Funnily enough, for once, Mum and Dad weren't cross with me at all!

25

Krazy Ketchup Splat!

Have fun making this fake ketchup splat to fool your family and friends with!

You will need:

- a board
- greaseproof paper
- tape
- bar of soap
- pen or pencil
- white craft glue
- dark red acrylic paint
- mixing spoon
- paintbrush
- palette or other blunt knife

Instructions

1. Tape the greaseproof paper firmly around the board.

2. Draw the outline of your splat on the greaseproof paper.

3. Rub the bar of soap on the greaseproof paper. This is important so that you can peel your splat off the paper later.

4. Mix ¼ cup of white glue with a couple of big splodges of red paint to make it the colour of ketchup.

5. Paint the red, gluey mixture on the paper in a thick layer, filling in your splat shape.

6. Let it dry for about a day.

7. When your splat feels dry, gently loosen the edges using a palette or other blunt knife and peel it off the paper.

8. Leave your splat to dry completely for another day.

TOP TIP! Your splat will take a couple of days to dry!

Countryside Wordsearch

Horrid Henry hates everything about the countryside, especially going walking with his family. Can you spot all the countryside words in the wordsearch puzzle below? Look up, down, backwards, forwards and diagonally.

beasts
nettles
quicksand
smells
exercise
goats
scenery
manure
cowpat
sheep
bulls
chickens
nature

s	s	s	s	t	a	s	y	g	e
t	h	l	a	c	e	t	h	o	r
s	e	s	l	l	e	m	s	a	u
a	e	o	t	u	m	n	e	t	n
e	p	t	a	n	b	d	e	s	a
b	e	c	o	w	p	a	t	r	m
n	e	x	e	r	c	i	s	e	y
s	n	e	k	c	i	h	c	w	a
t	d	n	a	s	k	c	i	u	q
c	h	t	v	e	r	u	t	a	n

Hidden in the wordsearch is a warning from Horrid Henry for anyone planning a nice walk in the countryside! You can find it by writing the remaining 20 letters in the spaces below.

_ !

Check out the answers on page 58.

The Basher – Headline News

Horrid Henry fills the latest edition of his best-selling newspaper, *The Basher*, with sensational stories about his family's disastrous days out.

WILD BULL ON THE LOOSE

The foolish parents who forced Henry to go on a hike in the countryside soon discovered they had made a big mistake when they were chased for miles by a savage bull.

"We could all have been killed," said Henry. "The countryside is a dangerous place."

His parents finally agreed and took Henry home to watch TV in safety. Whoopee! No more hiking!

CAR JOURNEY CHAOS

Henry's mean and miserable parents made him endure a car journey to attend a christening, instead of taking him to Rude Ralph's brilliant birthday party at Goo-Shooter World.

Events turned scary when Henry got locked in the toilet during a break.

"It was terrifying," said brave Henry, "but I finally managed to escape."

The endless journey continued, but *The Basher* can reveal that the parents had travelled to the christening on the wrong weekend, and so their son's hideous ordeal had all been for nothing.

SHOPPING SHOCKER

It was a shocking shopping experience when Henry's mum almost bought a pair of girls' trousers for Henry. Henry explained politely that it was not a good idea, but Mum screamed at him: "They are NOT girls' trousers."

The Basher says: "Mum came to her senses just in time when she saw a little girl in pigtails twirling around the shop in the very same trousers."

Result! Not only did Henry escape the girly trousers; Mum bought him some Root-a-Toot trainers instead.

The Basher says: "Well done, Mum. You made the right decision in the end."

WEDDING CAKE MYSTERY

Prissy Polly and Pimply Paul shocked their horrified wedding guests by not having a wedding cake. But *The Basher* can reveal that there WAS a wedding cake, with three layers and white icing. But it was no ordinary wedding cake. It was a talking cake!

Henry, a pageboy at the wedding, gave an exclusive interview to *The Basher*.

"It was very strange when the cake talked to me," he said. "It whispered, 'Eat me.' I couldn't be rude and ignore the cake – so I ate it."

Unfortunately for Henry, the groom did not believe in talking cakes.

The Big Weekend Quiz

 1. What does Horrid Henry love most about Saturdays at his house?

    a.   It's Sweet Day.

    b.   It's Watch-TV-All-Day Day.

    c.   It's Tidy-Your-Bedroom Day.

 2. Henry and Peter are rehearsing for a show at their Saturday morning dance class. What parts do they play?

    a.   Twirling tomatoes.

    b.   Pitter-patting raindrops.

    c.   Swaying bananas.

 3. What are the rules if you want to be in charge of the TV in Henry's house?

    a.   You have to be sitting on the sofa and have control of the TV remote.

    b.   You have to be sitting the closest to the TV.

    c.   You have to be sitting on the Comfy Black Chair and have control of the TV remote.

 4. Rude Ralph brings two shrunken heads with him when he comes to play. Henry tells Peter the heads are . . . ?

    a.   Mum and Dad.

    b.   Margaret and Susan.

    c.   Miss Battle-Axe and Miss Lovely.

 5. When Mum and Dad go out, Rabid Rebecca babysits for Henry and Peter. What is her secret fear?

    a.   Worms.

    b.   Hamsters.

    c.   Spiders.

 6. When Henry goes to the supermarket with Mum, he creates chaos. What does he do?

    a.   He rips open all the boxes of Sweet Tweet looking for a Gold Gizmo.

    b.   He squirts Krazy Ketchup all over Mum.

    c.   He shakes up a big bottle of fizzywizz, which explodes all over the shop.

7. When Henry plays with Peter's Curse of the Mummy Kit, who does he wrap up in toilet paper like a mummy?

    a.   Grandma and Fang.

    b.   Peter and Fluffy.

    c.   Rich Aunt Ruby and Stuck-up Steve.

 8. One boring, rainy weekend, Henry writes his will. What does he leave for Peter?

    a.   Sweet wrappers and a muddy twig.

    b.   His Purple Hand Gang flag.

    c.   Mr Kill.

 9. One weekend, Henry runs away to Moody Margaret's treehouse. What makes him go home?

    a.   He wants to watch *Hog House* on TV.

    b.   He misses Perfect Peter.

    c.   He smells pancakes cooking.

 10. When Henry and Margaret make Glop, which ingredient do they add?

    a.   Snails.

    b.   Porridge.

    c.   Bubble bath.

Check your score on page 58. How did you do?

 8-10:

WOWEE! You're a weekend whizzkid!

 6-7:

WELL DONE! You deserve a super Saturday!

 3-5:

WIMPY! What a poor score. Hand over your Saturday sweets!

 0-2:

WORSE and WORSE! It's a weekend of chores for you!

HORRID HENRY'S Computer

"The new computer is only for work," said Dad. "My work, Mum's work, and school work."

"Not for playing silly games," said Mum.

"But everyone plays games on their computer," said Henry.

"Not in this house," said Dad. He looked at the computer and frowned. "Hmmn," he said. "How do you turn this thing off?"

"Like this," said Horrid Henry. He pushed the "off" button.

"Aha," said Dad.

It was so unfair! Rude Ralph had Intergalactic Robot Rebellion. Dizzy Dave had Snake Masters Revenge III. Moody Margaret had Zippy Zappers. Horrid Henry had Be a Spelling Champion, Virtual Classroom, and Whoopee for Numbers. Aside from Beefy Bert, who'd been given Counting Made Easy for Christmas, no one else had such awful software.

"What's the point of finally getting a computer if you can't play games?" said Horrid Henry.

"You can improve your spelling," said Perfect Peter. "And write essays. I've already written one for school tomorrow."

"I don't want to improve my spelling!" screamed Henry. "I want to play games!"

"I don't," said Perfect Peter. "Unless it's 'Name that Vegetable' of course."

"Quite right, Peter," said Mum.

"You're the meanest parents in the world and I hate you," shrieked Henry.

"You're the best parents in the world and I love you," said Perfect Peter.

Horrid Henry had had enough. He leapt on Peter, snarling. He was the Loch Ness monster gobbling up a thrashing duck.

"OWWWWWW!" squealed Peter.

"Go to your room, Henry!" shouted Dad. "You're banned from the computer for a week."

"We'll see about that," muttered Horrid Henry, slamming his bedroom door.

Snore. Snore. Snore.

Horrid Henry sneaked past Mum and Dad's room and slipped downstairs.

There was the new computer. Henry sat down in front of it and looked longingly at the blank screen.

How could he get some games? He had 53p saved up. Not even enough for Snake Masters Revenge I, he thought miserably. Everyone he knew had fun on their computers. Everyone except him. He loved zapping aliens. He loved marshalling armies. He loved ruling the world. But no. His yucky parents would only let him have educational games. Ugh. When he was king anyone who wrote an educational game would be fed to the lions.

Horrid Henry sighed and switched on the computer. Maybe some games were hidden on the hard disk, he thought hopefully. Mum and Dad were scared of computers and wouldn't know how to look.

The word 'Password' flashed up on the screen.

I know a good password, thought Horrid Henry.

Find out what happens when Horrid Henry puts his own password on the family computer in 'Horrid Henry's Computer' in *Horrid Henry's Revenge*.

Crack the Computer Code

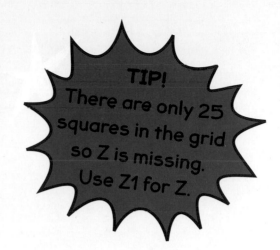

TIP!
There are only 25 squares in the grid so Z is missing. Use Z1 for Z.

Can you crack Henry's secret code and work out his new password for the family computer?

	1	2	3	4	5
a	c	o	m	p	u
b	t	e	r	a	b
c	d	f	g	h	i
d	j	k	l	n	q
e	s	v	w	x	y

Here is Henry's new computer password in code. Can you decode it?

**e1/a3/b2/d3/d3/e5
e1/a2/a1/d2/e1**

Invent your own secret code by completing the grid below. Fill in the first boxes with a word of your choice – Henry used the word 'computer' in his grid. Make sure your word doesn't have any 2 letters the same. Then fill in the rest of the letters of the alphabet in order. Now you can write your own top-secret passwords and messages.

	1	2	3	4	5
a					
b					
c					
d					
e					

Check out the answer on page 58.

The Grump Card Game

Henry's parents give out grump cards to Henry and Peter for exceptionally good behaviour.
The owner of a grump card can erase one punishment by giving back a grump card.
It's like a golden get-out-of-jail-free ticket!

START

You pull Peter's hair. 1 grump or go back 3 spaces.

You are rude to Dad. 1 grump or go back 5 spaces.

IT'S NOT FAIR!

GRUMP CARD — LEGAL TENDER

GRUMP CARD — LEGAL TENDER

You are caught scoffing sweets. 1 grump or go back to start.

GRUMP CARD — LEGAL TENDER

You spit out your sprouts. 1 grump or go back 3 spaces.

IT'S NOT FAIR!

GRUMP CARD — LEGAL TENDER

You flick peas at Peter. 1 grump or go back 3 spaces.

GRUMP CARD — LEGAL TENDER

You call Peter a popsicle. 1 grump or go back 4 spaces.

GRUMP CARD — LEGAL TENDER

You don't do homework. 1 grump or go back 4 spaces.

You pinch Peter. 1 grump or go back 7 spaces.

Instructions

1. Start with two grump cards.
2. The youngest player goes first.
3. Throw the dice and move your counter along the squares.
4. If you land on a GRUMP CARD square, pick up a grump card.
5. If you land on a blue square, give up a grump card or move back as instructed.
6. Follow the black arrows back if you land on an IT'S NOT FAIR! square.
7. The first player to the END wins.

You hide Bunnykins! 1 grump or go back 7 spaces.

You sneak on the computer. 1 grump or go back 3 spaces.

IT'S NOT FAIR!

Your room is messy. 1 grump or go back 6 spaces.

You sell Peter to Margaret! 1 grump or go back 5 spaces.

IT'S NOT FAIR!

You don't do your chores. 1 grump or go back 5 spaces.

You give your dad's boss a Dungeon Drink. 1 grump or go back 9 spaces.

END

HORRID HENRY'S
Left-out Wordsearch

Can you find all the family names in Henry's wordsearch below?
Look up, down, forwards, backwards and diagonally.

Dad
Henry
Grandma
Ruby
Greta
Steve
Grandpa
Vera
Mum
Polly
Paul
Granny

a	y	t	e	l	l	a	d
y	m	n	t	a	p	v	a
b	s	d	n	d	l	e	d
u	e	t	n	a	t	r	h
r	g	a	e	a	r	a	e
o	r	a	d	v	r	g	n
g	e	y	w	o	e	g	r
r	t	p	o	l	l	y	y
p	a	u	l	m	u	m	m

Henry has left out someone on purpose!
Find the hidden words from the leftover letters and guess who it is.

_ _ _ _ _ _ _ _ _ _   _ _ _ _ _   _ _ _

Horrid Henry left out _____

Check out the answers on page 58.

Funtastic food

THE BEST FOOD EVER

BEST BREAKFAST
Pancakes with lashings
of maple syrup

PERFECT PACKED LUNCH
Four packs of crisps, chocolate, doughnuts, cake,
lollies and sweets

1 grape

(Dad made me add some fruit)

DINNERS TO DIE FOR **
Spaghetti with meatballs, pizza, burger and chips,
ice cream, sweets

****Everything tastes a trillion times better
covered in yummy Krazy Ketchup and washed
down with fizzywizz!!**

THE MOST DISGUSTING FOOD IN THE WORLD
(or everything my parents try
to make me eat!!)

ALL vegetables, especially slimy string beans
and stomach-churning sprouts

ALL fruit, especially apples, ugh!

Muesli

Gloopy sauces with
green bits

White rubbery globules
of glop called
Cauliflower Cheese

Anything green and slimy
YEUUCH!!!

Mum witters on about healthy eating,
but I know her secret! She sneaks sweets
from the sweet jar, ha ha!

Match the missing words to make the names of my favourite sweets.

1. Blobby _ _ _ _ _ _ _ _   Balls
2. Nose   _ _ _ _ _ _ _ _   Blubbers
3. Dirt   _ _ _ _ _ _   Gobbers
4. Hot   _ _ _ _ _   Spiders
5. Rubber _ _ _ _ _ _ _ _ _ _ Snot
6. Spiky   _ _ _ _ _ _ _ _   Pickers

Check out the answers on page 58.

Muddy Maze

MUM →

DAD →

Horrid Henry and his family are hiking in the countryside.
Who finds their way to the end of the walk without ending up in a cowpat?

HENRY

PETER

END

Check out the answer on page 59.

Favourite Family Games

It's family game time and each member of the family has picked a game to play. See if you can guess who has picked which game!

SWEETIE SCAVENGER HUNT

You will need:
Loads of brilliant sweets, like Big Boppers, Belcher Squelchers and Chocolate Spitballs.

How to play
1. Hide the sweets around the house.
2. Give each player a list of the sweets they have to find.
3. Send the players off to scavenge for sweets.
4. The winner is the player who finds the most sweets.

1. WHOSE GAME?
_____

THE SUITCASE GAME
A lovely way to learn your alphabet!

How to play
1. The first player thinks of a word beginning with the letter 'a' – like 'apple' – and says: "I packed my suitcase with an apple."
2. The second player thinks of a word beginning with 'b' – like 'Bunnykins' – and says: "I packed my suitcase with an apple and Bunnykins."
3. The game continues with letters 'c', 'd', 'e', and so on.
4. If a player can't think of a word or forgets the list, they are out.
5. The game continues until only one player – the winner – is left.

2. WHOSE GAME?
_____

TASTE THE FRUIT AND VEG

You will need:
- Small pieces of a few different fruits and vegetables
- Scarves

How to play

1. Tie the scarves around each player's eyes.
2. Feed each player with a piece of a mystery fruit or vegetable.
3. The players have to guess what they are eating.
4. The winner is the player who guesses the most fruit and veg correctly.

4. WHOSE GAME?

_____

ANIMAL CHARADES

You will need:
- Cut-out pictures of animal pictures or photos
- A bucket or a bowl

How to play

1. Fold up the animal pictures and put them in the bucket.
2. Players take it in turns to pull a picture out of the bucket, and act out the animal. IMPORTANT RULE: NO ANIMAL NOISES ALLOWED.
3. The other players have to guess which animal it is.
4. The winner is the player who guesses the most animals.

3. WHOSE GAME?

_____

Check out the answers on page 59.   41

Gross Grub Sudoku

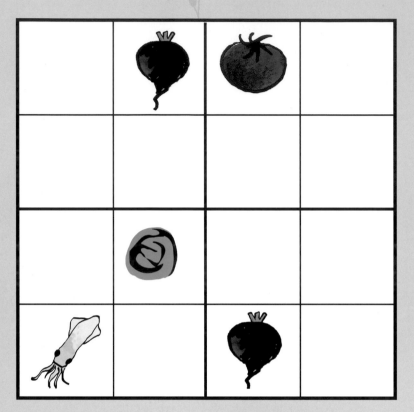

Fill in the sudoku so that every square and row – both up and down – contains a picture of the food that Henry or his family members hate. Peter can't bear beetroot, Mum dislikes squid, Dad detests tomatoes and Henry hates sprouts.

Try a trickier one! Fill in every square and row with the numbers 1-6.

TOP TIP: Fill in all the 6s first, followed by the 4s.

	5	3	6		
			4	5	
		4		1	
6			2	4	
3					2
2		6			

Find the answers on page 59.

Picture Crossword

You can find all the crossword answers in the picture of Henry at home.

CLUES

Across

2. The toy on the floor in front of Fluffy is called a GOO _____ ?

5. What colour are Fluffy's eyes?

Down

1. Henry's favourite catalogue is called _____ HEAVEN?

2. What is the creature hidden in the jam jar?

3. How many desk drawers can you count?

4. What colour clothes are Henry and Peter wearing in the photos on the wall?

The answers are on page 60.

HORRID HENRY'S Horrid Weekend

Ding dong.

Horrid Henry, Perfect Peter, Mum and Dad stood outside Rich Aunt Ruby's enormous house on a grey, drizzly day. Steve opened the massive front door.

"Oh," he sneered. "It's you."

Steve opened the present Mum had brought. It was a small flashlight. Steve put it down.

"I already have a much better one," he said.

"Oh," said Mum.

Another boy stood beside him. A boy who looked vaguely familiar. A boy . . . Horrid Henry gasped. Oh no. It was Bill. Bossy Bill. The horrible son of Dad's boss. Henry had once tricked Bill into photocopying his bottom. Bill had sworn revenge. Horrid Henry's insides turned to jelly. Trust Stuck-up Steve to be friends with Bossy Bill. It was bad enough being trapped in a house with one Arch-Enemy. Now he was stuck in a house with TWO . . .

Stuck-Up Steve scowled at Henry. "You're wearing that old shirt of mine," he said. "Don't your parents ever buy you new clothes?"

Bossy Bill snorted.

"Steve," said Aunt Ruby. "Don't be rude."

"I wasn't," said Steve. "I was just asking. No harm in asking, is there?"

"No," said Horrid Henry. He smiled at Steve. "So when will Aunt Ruby buy you a new face?"

"Henry," said Mum. "Don't be rude."

"I was just asking," said Henry. "No harm in asking, is there?" he added, glaring at Steve.

Steve glared back.

Aunt Ruby beamed. "Henry, Steve and Bill are taking you to their friend Tim's paintballing party."

"Won't that be fun," said Mum.

Peter looked frightened.

"Don't worry, Peter," said Aunt Ruby, "you can help me plant seedlings while the older boys are out."

Peter beamed. "Thank you," he said. "I don't like paintballing. Too messy and scary."

Paintballing! Horrid Henry loved paintballing. The chance to splat Steve and Bill with ooey gooey globs of paint ... hmmm, maybe the weekend was looking up.

Find out how Henry gets along with Steve and Bill in 'Horrid Henry's Horrid Weekend' in *Horrid Henry's Monster Movie*.

Are You a Gruesome Guest?

Follow the flowchart and find out.

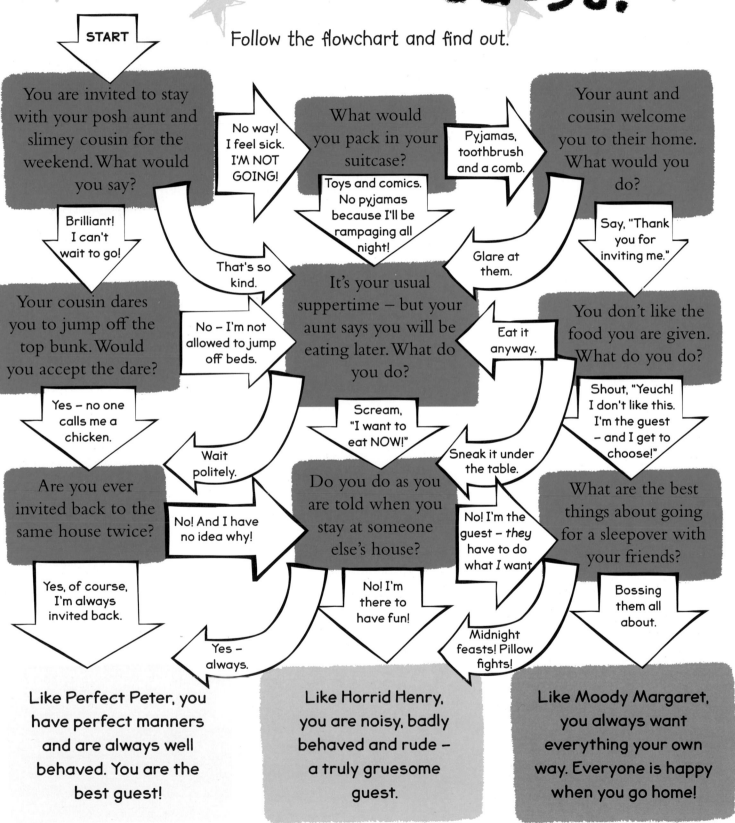

HORRiD HENRY'S Autobiography

How well do you know Horrid Henry?
He's written an autobiography, but some of the words are missing.
Can you fill in the right answers in the blanks from the options below?

Lord High Excellent Majesty of the ————— 1 ————— Gang, leader and boss of the secret fort and the destroyer of the ————— 2 ————— and Nappy Noodle Brothers. Wizard, star actor, footballer, trickster, genius, the scourge of evil enemies and the bulldozer of babysitters and battle-axes and demon dinner ladies and horrible cousins. I was born in ————— 3 ————— – oh, let's skip that boring bit – to the King and Queen, but sadly I was stolen by an evil wizard and dumped with . . . THEM. Obviously I am waiting for my real parents to collect me and take me back to the palace, but until then I am stuck with the world's most ————— ————— 4 —————and ————— parents in the history of the world.

1.
a. Purple Hand
b. Yellow Hand
c. Green Lion
d. Purple Foot

2.
a. Undercover Club
b. Secret Society
c. Secret Club
d. Keep Out Club

3.
a. January
b. February
c. March
d. April

4.
a. charming, nice and lovely
b. funny, generous and caring
c. smart, rich and understanding
d. boring, mean and horrible

5.

a. Peter
b. Paul
c. Phillip
d. Picasso

6.

a. deadly daring dumb dinosaur
b. nappy noodle poopy pants
c. evil little smarty pants
d. handsome green froggy frog

7.

a. giant
b. hamster
c. king
d. wizard

8.

a. great reader
b. impressive hiker
c. genius trickster
d. celebrated cook

To say nothing of their son, the worm, my so-called younger brother, ———. As if someone as amazing as me could have such a ——— ——— ——— for a brother. That just proves I must have been stolen by a ———. There is no other possible explanation. My greatest talent, among so many, is that I am a ——— ———. I have played so many amazing, fantastic tricks that it's hard for even me to remember them all!

Check page 60 to see if you were right!

Family Jokes Double Puzzle

Match the words to the family's favourite jokes and complete the punchlines.

HORRID HENRY

1. What happens when you play table tennis with a rotten egg?

First it goes ping, then it goes

_ _ _ _ _ .

PERFECT PETER

2. What kind of music do balloons hate?

_ _ _ .

STUCK-UP STEVE

5. What's a shark's favourite game?

_ _ _ _ _ **and seek.**

DAD

3. How do you make a really good milkshake?

Tell it a _ _ _ _ _ _ **story.**

RICH AUNT RUBY

6. Why did the queen draw straight lines?

Because she was the

_ _ _ _ _ _ .

MUM

4. What did the mummy broom say to the baby broom?

It's time to go to _ _ _ _ _ _ .

GRANDMA

7. Why are false teeth like stars?

Because they come out at

_ _ _ _ _ _ .

PRISSY POLLY

8. Why do mice need oiling?

Because they _ _ _ _ _ _ _ _ .

48

Now see if you can fit the same words
into the criss-cross puzzle too.

3 letters
pop

4 letters
pong
bite

5 letters
scary
sweep
ruler
night

6 letters
squeak

Check out the answers on page 60.

HORRID HENRY'S Hobbies

Everyone knows that Horrid Henry likes watching TV, scoffing chocolate, crisps and sweets, and zapping aliens on the computer. But he has lots of other hobbies too!

COLLECTING

👍 Collecting Gizmos from cereal packets is good fun because I get to eat loads of Sweet Tweet!

👎 Copycat Peter collects them too, worse luck, and Mum makes us take turns to have the Gizmo.

MUSIC

👍 I love music - the louder the better. The Killer Boy Rats are my best band.

👎 My miserable Mum and Dad shout at me to turn the music down, even when I tell them it's helping me to concentrate on my homework.

FAN CLUB

👍 I am a member of the *Gross-Out* Fan Club because *Gross-Out* is the best TV programme in the world. It has ice-cream eating contests and goo-shooting shoot-outs!

👎 My stinky parents think it's a disgusting programme and turn it off.

READING

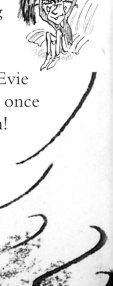

👍 Comics are great, but I like reading books too, as long as it's a Skeleton Skunk or Evil Evie book.

👎 My useless parents think that Evil Evie encourages me to be horrid, and they once took away all my books. What rubbish!

Spot the Difference

One of Horrid Henry's hobbies is making lots of noise.
Can you spot 6 differences between the 2 pictures?

1. _____

2. _____

3. _____

4. _____

5. _____

6. _____

Check the answers on page 60.

True or False?

Is Henry always horrid? Is Peter always perfect?
Try this quiz and see if you can guess which statements are true and which are false!

1. Perfect Peter unwound all the strings of his cello
   so he wouldn't have to do his practice.

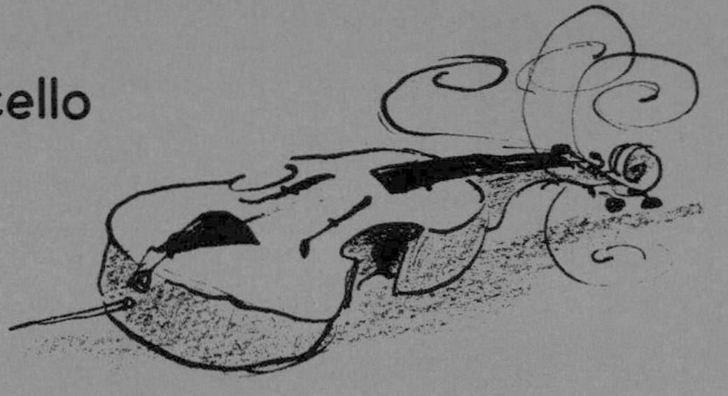

   TRUE? ☐   FALSE? ☐

2. Horrid Henry once said: "Dad, you look tired. Can I help get
   supper ready?"

   TRUE? ☐   FALSE? ☐

3. Perfect Peter poured cat litter all over Horrid Henry.

   TRUE? ☐   FALSE? ☐

4. Horrid Henry threw a plate of spaghetti and
   tomato sauce at Mum.

   TRUE? ☐   FALSE? ☐

5. Perfect Peter ate a big greasy lunch of sausages and chips
   and threw up all over Dad.

   TRUE? ☐   FALSE? ☐

6. Horrid Henry helped at home by shampooing the carpet.

   TRUE? ☐   FALSE? ☐

7. Perfect Peter hid a muddy twig in Henry's bed.

TRUE? ☐   FALSE? ☐

8. Horrid Henry took a bite out of all the chocolates in the box, and then offered them to Grandma.

TRUE? ☐   FALSE? ☐

9. Perfect Peter serves Rotten Crispies, Nasty Nuts and Dungeon Drinks to Mum and Dad's dinner guests.

TRUE? ☐   FALSE? ☐

10. Horrid Henry happily ate snails at Restaurant Le Posh – without screaming and shouting.

TRUE? ☐   FALSE? ☐

Check your score on page 60.

 7-10:

Well done! A fantastic fib-busting score!

 4-6

A pathetic score, you puny pants face!

 0-3:

Rats, that's really rubbish. Have another go!

Oh, No! It's Bedtime!

Henry hates the word 'bedtime', almost as much as 'homework' and 'vegetables'.
But even King Henry the Horrible has to go to bed.

HENRY'S BEDTIME PLAN

1. Have a bubble bath – very deep and very hot!

Make tidal waves, dive for buried treasure, fight sea monsters and stage battles with Snappy Croc and Yellow Duck. Paint the walls with soapy suds and make bubble-bath beards. Brilliant fun!! Best thing of all - Peter can't spoil my games in the bath or get me into trouble. But sometimes Dad makes me share with Peter. It's NOT fair! Peter likes the water freezing. I make sure Peter gets squished by the taps. Nah nah ne na nah!

2. Bedtime at eight! It's not fair!

My stinky, horrible parents say that my bedtime is at eight – with lights out at eight-thirty. All my favourite programmes are on then. I can't miss *Cannibal Cook!* Rude Ralph goes loads later than eight!!

3. Make a protest.

Lie on the floor, kicking and screaming, "I'm not tired! I won't go to bed!"

4. Go upstairs.

Drag my feet as I stagger up the stairs to my bedroom.

5. Teeth.

Brush my teeth very slowly.

6. Pyjamas.

Take hours putting on my pyjamas.

7. Brilliant delaying tactic.

Tell Mum and Dad I still need to do my homework.

8. Another delaying tactic.

Ask for endless drinks of water.

9. Banished to bed but still not beaten!

Read comics under the covers with my trusty torch, tee hee!

PERFECT PETER'S BEDTIME ROUTINE

1. Bathtime.

I don't like sharing my bath with Henry. He likes the water much too hot. And he makes me sit by the taps – they hurt my back. Clever Dad has made a new house rule: the person who sits by the taps decides the temperature. That'll teach Henry to be so horrid. Then Henry told me about the plughole monster. It sneaks up the drain while you're having a bath, slithers through the plughole and sucks children down. Now I'm too scared to sit near the taps!

2. Storytime.

Mum or Dad read me a nice, unscary story – my favourite bedtime book is *Sammy the Snuggly Snail*.

3. Lights out.

I love settling down with Bunnykins, my favourite cuddly toy, and Snoozie Whoozie, a bunny that giggles me to sleep. Henry can't sleep without his teddy, Mr Kill, but he doesn't want anyone to know – OOPS!

WHAT'S YOUR BEDTIME ROUTINE?

BEDTIME? _____

LIGHTS OUT? _____

CUDDLY TOY? _____

FAVOURITE STORY? _____

Plughole Monster Picture

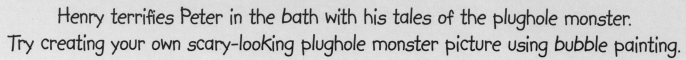

Henry terrifies Peter in the bath with his tales of the plughole monster.
Try creating your own scary-looking plughole monster picture using *bubble* painting.

You will need

- newspaper
- white paper
- washing-up liquid or bubble bath
- poster paints
- water
- tablespoon
- empty yoghurt pots or other containers
- thick straws
- black felt-tipped pen

Instructions

1. Gently place your piece of paper on top of the carton, and move the paper around so that the paint from the bubbles is transferred to the paper, and leaves a bubble pattern.
2. Repeat this until you've covered your paper. Add different colours if you like.
3. Leave your bubble painting until it is completely dry.
4. Finally, using the black felt-tipped pen, draw your monster among the bubbles.
5. Protect your work surface with newspaper.
6. Squirt some poster paint into a yoghurt pot, and stir in about 1 centimetre of water and 2 tablespoons of washing-up liquid or bubble bath.
7. Put a straw in the paint mixture and blow out until bubbles rise above the top of the carton.

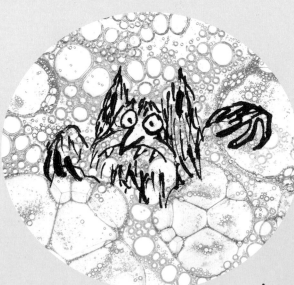

Look! It's crawling out of the plughole to scare Perfect Peter!

See you next year!

ANSWERS

Page 11

There are 10 Baa Baa Sheepies on pages 19, 21, 24, 31, 34, 38, 43, 46, 49, 55. Fluff Puff is on page 55.

Pages 14-15

1. Rich Aunt Ruby

2. Stuck-up Steve

3. Mum

4. Great-Aunt Greta

5. Prissy Polly

6. Pimply Paul

7. Dad

8. Perfect Peter

Pages 18-19

1 = A

2 = D

3 = E

4 = B

5 = G

6 = C

7 = F

Page 23

	HOW MUCH POCKET MONEY?	DREAM TOY
HORRID HENRY	50p	Hip-Hop Robot Dog
MOODY MARGARET	£5.00	Demon Dagger Sabre
STUCK-UP STEVE	£10.00	Super-Blooper Blaster

Page 27

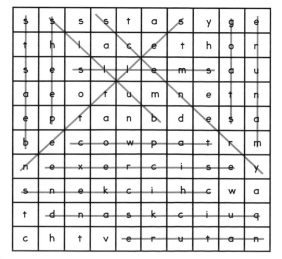

Horrid Henry's hidden message is:

stay at home and watch tv!

Pages 30-31

1. **a**

2. **b**

3. **c**

4. **b**

5. **c**

6. **a**

7. **b**

8. **a**

9. **c**

10. **b**

Page 33

Henry's password is:

smelly socks

Page 36

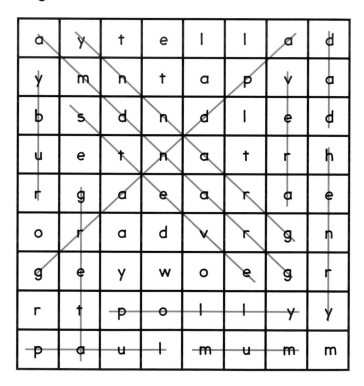

The leftover letters are: **telltale toady worm**

Horrid Henry left out **Peter.**

Page 37

1. Blobby Gobbers

2. Nose Pickers

3. Dirt Balls

4. Hot Snot

5. Rubber Blubbers

6. Spiky Spiders

Pages 38-39

Only Horrid Henry reaches the end of the walk.

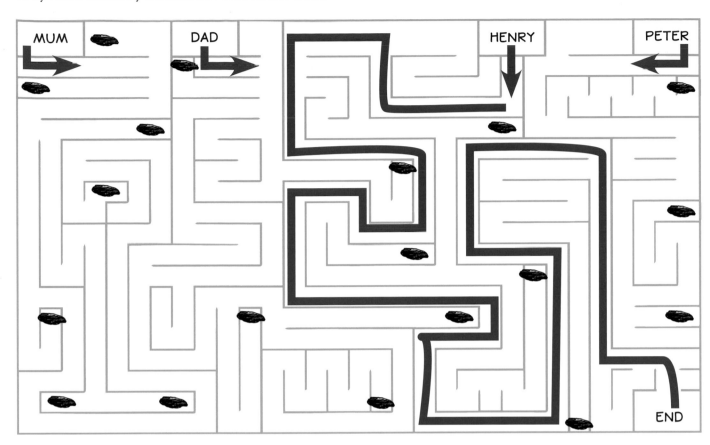

Pages 40-41

1. Horrid Henry's

3. Mum's

2. Perfect Peter's

4. Dad's

Page 42

4	5	3	6	2	1
1	6	2	4	5	3
5	2	4	3	1	6
6	3	1	2	4	5
3	4	5	1	6	2
2	1	6	5	3	4

Page 43

		¹t				
²s	h	o	o	³t	e	r
p		y		h		
i				r		⁴p
d				e		i
e		⁵g	r	e	e	n
r						k

Pages 46-47

1. a

2. c

3. b

4. d

5. a

6. b

7. d

8. c

Pages 48-49

1. pong

2. pop

3. scary

4. sweep

5. bite

6. ruler

7. night

8. squeak

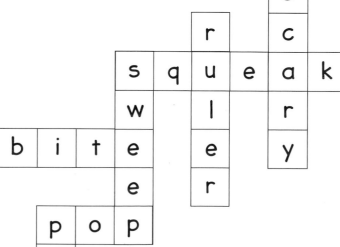

Page 51

1. Sweet missing

2. Car is blue

3. Lines missing from page of book on bed

4. Sound line missing from speaker

5. Plane wing is solid red

6. One of the skull's eyes is missing

Pages 52-53

1. FALSE – It was Henry who did this in 'Horrid Henry Rocks'.

2. TRUE – Henry really did offer to help in 'Horrid Henry's Perfect Day'.

3. FALSE – Peter wanted to do this in 'Horrid Henry's Cannibal Curse' but he didn't dare do it.

4. FALSE – It was Peter who did this in 'Horrid Henry's Perfect Day'.

5. TRUE – Peter did this in 'Horrid Henry's Holiday'.

6. TRUE – Henry did this in 'Horrid Henry's Bad Book'.

7. FALSE – Peter thought about doing this to get revenge on Henry in 'Perfect Peter's Revenge', but he decided to do something far worse instead!

8. FALSE – It was Peter who did this in 'Perfect Peter's Horrid Day'.

9. FALSE – Henry did this in 'Horrid Henry and the Dinner Guests'.

10. TRUE – Henry really enjoyed eating snails in 'Horrid Henry Dines at Restaurant Le Posh'.